E

Thoreau, Henry Dav

What befell at Mrs
Brooks's

DATE			
FEB 3 '78	AUG 11 '78	FEB 9 '99	
MAR 10 '78	APR 17 '90	MAR 4 '9	
MAY 5 '78	NOV 5 '90	JUL 15 '92	
	JAN 15 '78	MAY 5 '92	
JUN 2 '78	MAY 13 '83	NOV 1 6 '92	
JUN 23 '78	JUN 3 '84	MAY 1 9 '92	
		MAY 14 '99	
	NO 1 4 '84	MAR 2 0 2	
JUL 7 '78		NOV 2 8 2000	
	JAN 3 0 '95	MAY 2 2 00	
JAN 28 '83	OCT 6 '86	DEC 0 1 09	
	NOV 2 1 '88		

What Befell
at Mrs. Brooks's

WHAT BEFELL
AT
MRS. BROOKS'S

by Henry D. Thoreau

pictures by George A. Overlie

 Lerner Publications Company · MINNEAPOLIS, MINNESOTA

This edition first published 1974 by Lerner Publications Company
Illustrations copyright © 1974 by George Overlie
All rights reserved. Printed in U.S.A.
ISBN: 0-8225-0284-4
LIBRARY OF CONGRESS CATALOG CARD NUMBER: 72-13329

E
C.1

Thoreau's Journal, March 19, 1856

On the morning of the 17th,

Mrs. Brooks's Irish girl Joan fell down the cellar stairs, and was found by her mistress lying at the bottom, apparently lifeless.

Mrs. Brooks ran
to the street-door
for aid to get her up,

and asked a
Miss Farmer,
who was
passing,
to call
the blacksmith near by.

The latter lady turned
instantly, and, making
haste across the road
on this errand,
fell flat
in a puddle of melted snow,

and came back
to Mrs. Brooks's,
bruised and dripping
and asking for
opodeldoc.

Mrs. Brooks again
ran to the door
and called to
George Bigelow
to complete
the unfinished errand.

He ran nimbly
about it
and fell flat
in another puddle
near the former,

but, his joints
being limber,
got along without
opodeldoc
and raised the blacksmith.

He also
notified
James Burke,
who was passing,

and he, rushing in
to render aid,
fell off one side
of the cellar stairs in the dark.

They no sooner
got the girl up-stairs
than she came to

and went raving,

then had a fit.

Haste makes waste.

It never rains

but it pours.

I have this from those
who have heard
Mrs. Brooks's story,
seen the girl,
the stairs,
and the puddles.

The New England writer Henry David Thoreau was born on July 12, 1817, in Concord, Massachusetts. It was here that Thoreau earned his reputation as a writer, a philosopher, and a lover of nature. In his essays and lectures, his poems and books, Thoreau glorified the individual who lives in harmony with nature and who follows his own conscience. He wrote on similar topics in his journals, which he kept for many years. In one of his journals Thoreau recorded the story of "What Befell at Mrs. Brooks's," a humorous incident reflecting a common human failing.